# CONTENTS

# Welcome to the Hunterian Museum

The Hunterian Museum is a world-class surgical heritage resource at the heart of the Royal College of Surgeons. The collections, together with this book, tell the fascinating story of surgeons and surgery over the last three centuries.

This guidebook introduces the surgeon-anatomist John Hunter, who amassed the most comprehensive collection of human and animal anatomy specimens in 18th-century Europe, and explains how his museum came to be in the Royal College of Surgeons.

'It is incredible how vast the museum is,' wrote one contemporary admirer, 'John Hunter takes in everything.' Yet Hunter's captivating specimens are only part of the College's holdings. There are fine and decorative arts on display, including many portraits, and rich research collections held in store: archives that illuminate the history of healthcare, a treasury of historical instruments and an outstanding odontological collection of teeth and bones.

These collections engage audiences with the past, present and future of surgery. They provide learning opportunities for thousands of visitors from school groups to surgical trainees, and researchers come from all over the world to use them.

I hope you enjoy your visit.

**Sam Alberti**
*Director of Museums and Archives*

# CHAPTER ONE

# Before Hunter

The science of anatomy has its roots in the
Renaissance but until the 18th century knowledge
of the body had little impact on surgical practice.
John Hunter used anatomical knowledge in surgery.

When you walk into the Hunterian Museum the most striking feature is the Crystal Gallery: eight floor-to-ceiling glass cases containing over 3,000 preparations from John Hunter's collection. They include human and animal remains showing healthy anatomical structures as well as those affected by illness and injury. John Hunter used them to teach the intricate structures of the human body, an essential part of medical education.

Although dissecting the human body to understand its anatomy dates back to ancient times, it was culturally and spiritually taboo in the Western and Islamic world until the Renaissance. In 1543 Andreas Vesalius published *De humani corporis fabrica (On the Fabric of the Human Body)*, which was directly based on dissections. Illustrating his work with detailed drawings, Vesalius encouraged students of anatomy to carry out their own dissections and to make close observations of what they found. John Hunter would later urge his pupils to follow Vesalius's example and take a practical approach to their studies. 'But why think,' he asked his protégé Edward Jenner, 'why not try the experiment?'

In Britain, Vesalius's work coincided with the merger of the Company of Barbers and the Guild of Surgeons to form the Company of Barber-Surgeons. Under a 1540 Royal Charter granted by Henry VIII the combined Company was given permission to dissect the bodies of four convicted criminals each year. However, these dissections were not particularly educational, instead they were public spectacles intended to deter crime, which happened to provide some gruesome public entertainment as well.

From the middle of the 18th century there were more opportunities to carry out dissections in Britain. At private anatomy schools each student worked on an individual corpse and through systematic dissection learnt the intricate structure of the human body, making him a better surgeon.

Yet surgery remained a crude practice at this time. Pain relief was minimal and standards of hygiene were poor because there was little understanding of infections. Surgeons were largely confined to treating superficial injuries, dressing wounds, extracting teeth and letting blood. Only as a last resort would a patient submit to a major operation such as an amputation or a lithotomy (bladder stone removal), and survival rates were very low. Surgeons confined themselves to techniques that had been taught for many centuries, passing this knowledge from one generation to the next through hands-on apprenticeships.

Hunter was one of a number of surgeons who studied and collected anatomy in order to replace established approaches with new surgical techniques based on sound anatomical knowledge and experimentation. And yet their collections were not just used for medical study. In the 16th and 17th centuries anatomical models and preparations of human remains became popular items for private collectors. Elaborate figures in ivory and other materials may have had medical uses but they were also valued as beautiful objects with moral purposes as *memento mori* to remind the wealthy of the inevitability of death.

Human remains were displayed alongside other collectable objects. London physician and antiquary Hans Sloane (1660–1753) included over 700 anatomical preparations among his collection of antiquities, coins and natural history. Sloane's collection would become the basis for the British Museum but some of his specimens can be found in the Hunterian Museum today.

**Ivory Anatomical Models**
16th or 17th-century Italian models showing the internal structures of the male and female body.

## Evelyn Tables

Four anatomical tables produced by Giovanni Leoni d'Este, dissector to Johann Vesling, Professor of Anatomy in Padua. Purchased by John Evelyn in 1646 and given to the Royal Society in 1676; later transferred to the British Museum and purchased by the College in 1809.

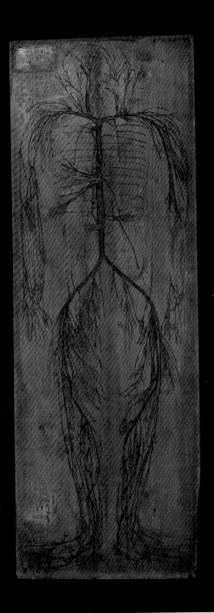
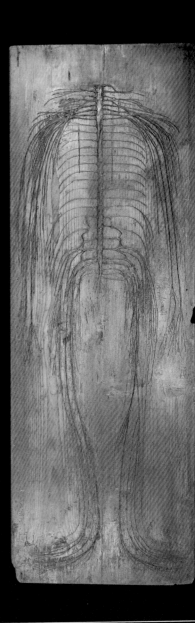

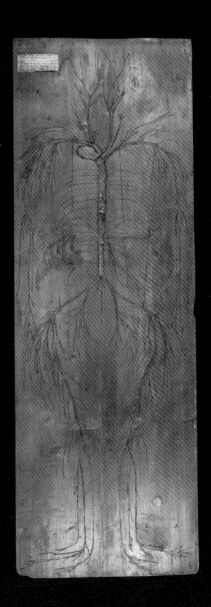

# CHAPTER TWO

# John Hunter

John Hunter was one of the founders of scientific surgery. He brought an experimental approach to surgical practice and his museum is a lasting record of his pioneering work.

John Hunter was born in 1728 near Glasgow, the youngest of ten children. As a child he enjoyed being outdoors and working with his hands. His elder brother William, who studied divinity at Glasgow University, was quite different: nevertheless, their paths were to run in parallel. William went into medicine, moving to London to study anatomy and midwifery. He soon set up his own anatomy school in Covent Garden and in 1748 John journeyed south to assist him.

For over a decade they worked together. William built up a reputation as a physician, man-midwife and lecturer while John developed considerable skills in dissection and a detailed knowledge of anatomy. William encouraged John to train as a surgeon and so he became a pupil of two of the most renowned hospital surgeons of the time,

William Cheselden in Chelsea and Percivall Pott at St Bartholomew's.

In 1760 John enrolled as a military surgeon and served for two years in France and Portugal. There he developed new ideas on the treatment of gunshot wounds and venereal disease that would later become the basis for important books. He also began to collect material for what was to be the finest anatomical collection of its time. His combined experience of dissecting, collecting specimens and wartime surgery sparked an interest in the functions of the body that would continue for the rest of his life.

Hunter returned to London as an experienced surgeon. William's school was now thriving but the brothers' relationship was uneasy and John chose to set up as a dental surgeon, even though dentists were then regarded with suspicion by many surgeons. He also gave lectures and began to take on pupils, many of whom went on to be prominent surgeons in their own right.

Like any aspiring surgeon, John wanted to gain a permanent position at one of London's hospitals. Finally in 1768 he was elected to be a surgeon at St George's Hospital on Hyde Park Corner where he had been a pupil and junior surgeon. Although his new position had no salary, it boosted his private practice and provided ample material for research. By this time he had achieved considerable renown as an anatomist and had been elected to the Royal Society and to the Company of Surgeons (which had split from the Barber-Surgeons). He was later appointed Surgeon Extraordinary to George III and Surgeon General of the army.

In 1771, with his status and income secure, John married Anne Home, the daughter of a fellow army officer. Anne was an accomplished poet who moved in artistic and literary circles with contacts that would help John's career. They divided their time between a townhouse on Jermyn Street and the country estate at Earl's Court that John had purchased in 1765. Earl's Court was still a village outside the city at the time and John had built a sizeable villa where he carried out experiments and kept an exotic menagerie including ostriches and leopards.

In 1783 the Hunters moved into a large property on Leicester Square. Here John dissected, taught and researched, while Anne held soirées for polite society. Her guests included the writers James Boswell and

Horace Walpole and the composer Joseph Haydn, who set some of her poems to music.

The property also included a large space for Hunter's collection. Like his brother William, whose collections are now in the University of Glasgow, John had gathered one of the largest anatomical museums in Europe. Among the 14,000 specimens were preparations to illustrate 'normal' (healthy) human anatomy and 'morbid' (diseased) specimens, many of which can be seen in the Hunterian Museum's Crystal Gallery today.

**John Hunter by Sir Joshua Reynolds, 1786**
Anne Hunter persuaded her husband to sit for Reynolds. He is in a philosophical pose, with books and specimens from his collection.

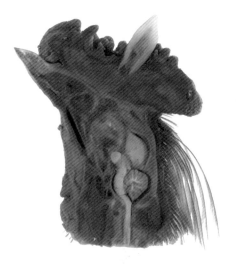

**A Transplanted Tooth**
The result of one of Hunter's more
unusual experiments: a healthy
human tooth grafted into the
comb on the head of a cockerel.

**The Dissecting Room**

This drawing by Thomas Rowlandson, probably from the late 18th century, is likely to show William Hunter's anatomy school. Certainly the upper figure in spectacles bears his resemblance. Surgeons and anatomists were often the subject of criticism and caricature in this period.

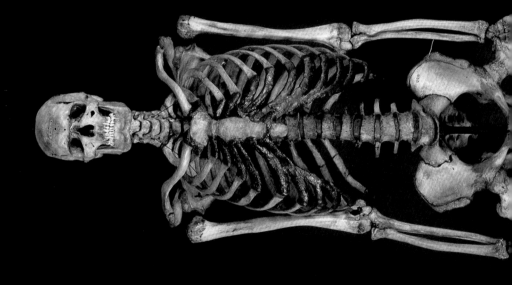

7ft 7"

5ft 7"

Average height
of a man in the
18th century

**Charles Byrne, the 'Irish Giant'**
Charles Byrne had a condition that caused him to grow to seven feet seven inches tall. His skeleton is now in the museum to demonstrate unusual bone growth and it is one of the best-known exhibits.

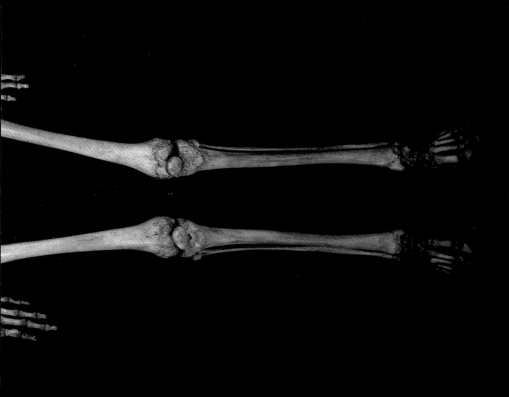

John Hunter was fascinated with the 'animal oeconomy' (which today would be termed physiology), which is why this medical museum has so much natural history. He carefully analysed the structure of 400 species from all over the world. He received casualties from the Royal Menagerie and a bottlenose whale that had swum up the Thames. His friend, the famous naturalist Sir Joseph Banks, brought him rare specimens such as kangaroos from James Cook's voyage, and the explorer William Paterson brought him a mounted giraffe from Africa. This was the first giraffe to be exhibited in Britain but as it was too big to fit in Hunter's townhouse he sawed off its legs! Only after the Hunters moved to Leicester Square could the giraffe finally be displayed whole.

Hunter split his collection into two main classes. The first showed the relationship between bodily structures and functions such as motion and digestion. These preparations were arranged to show a progression from simple to complex forms. The second class demonstrated 'generation': the reproduction and development of plants and animals. In his notes Hunter wrote that this 'production of animals out of themselves excites wonder, admiration and curiosity.' His collection also included the results of his ceaseless experiments on regeneration, transplantation and how animal structures adapt to external factors such as injury or disease.

Injuries and disease featured in the human preparations too. They include the preserved leg of a coachman who had his femoral artery tied off by Hunter in order to cure his popliteal aneurysm (a painful swollen artery in his leg that might have led to amputation).

The coachman long outlived the surgeon. Morbid human remains – which now would be termed 'pathological' – accounted for around 2,000 of Hunter's preparations. Their pots were labelled with a history of the case or with the name of the patient, and he used them extensively in his teaching to demonstrate particular conditions. Some came from dissections in his anatomy school or at St George's Hospital. Others were from the bodies of wealthy private patients, or given to Hunter by other surgeons. Like other anatomists he regularly bought human remains either as dead bodies – including Charles Byrne, the 'Irish Giant' – or as preparations auctioned by other anatomists.

Most of the collection, however, was carefully crafted by Hunter himself. Much work and skill went into making the specimens. He stored them in glass jars, suspended on threads to stop the specimen sinking to the bottom. The majority were preserved in alcohol. The tops were sealed with layers of pig's bladder, tin and lead, and then painted over with pitch. In the 19th century cut glass lids were fitted, mainly because students kept putting their fingers through the lids of the jars. Over time the alcohol evaporates and discolours and needs to be replaced, so each jar has to be opened, refilled and re-sealed – it remains hard work to keep them in good condition today.

Not all of the specimens are in alcohol: some were preserved in oil of turpentine, while others have been transferred into plastic containers with modern preservatives such as glycerine. Hunter also made specimens by allowing soft tissues and bones to dry, and then varnishing them. These had their own problems – they were very attractive to beetles, which would eat them if they were left uncovered. Later additions include intricate 'corrosion casts', which used wax to provide stunning (but very fragile) moulds of vessels.

The effort that went into such a vast collection tells us much about John's character. He rose at five o'clock and worked in his dissecting room for several hours; during the day he taught and saw patients before writing in the evening. He was renowned for his abrupt manners and given to bouts of temper. In 1780 he and William argued over which of them had discovered the circulation of the placenta, and they remained estranged until William died in 1783. John, meanwhile, suffered from angina. In 1793, at an especially heated meeting at St George's, Hunter collapsed and died of a heart attack. Although he wanted his diseased heart to be preserved, his remains are not in the museum. John Hunter is now buried in Westminster Abbey but his legacy lives on in the Royal College of Surgeons.

**Spirit Specimen**
John Hunter gave this preserved intestine to King George III for the royal teaching collection. Hunter injected it to show the blood vessels.

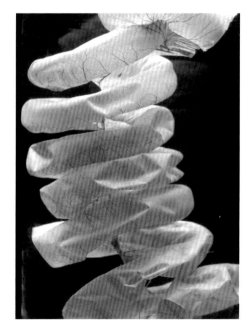

## Hunter's House

In 1783 John Hunter leased two houses at 28 Leicester Square and 13 Castle Street. Between them he erected a new building containing a lecture theatre, a 'conversazione room' for scientific meetings, and a museum. The main house was renovated as a fashionable family home while Castle Street was modified to provide dissecting rooms and accommodation for his pupils. The layout was inspired by William Hunter's anatomy school in Great Windmill Street, which had been designed by their brother-in-law, the architect Robert Mylne.

The museum provided a physical barrier between the social spaces in the Leicester Square house and the dissecting rooms in Castle Street. At the same time it allowed visitors to see anatomical preparations used in teaching alongside other kinds of collectable objects. This helped to reinforce the idea that anatomy was part of a broader interest in natural philosophy and the arts.

### 28 Leicester Square

The drawing room on the first floor of the main house was used by Anne Hunter for her weekly salons. It was lavishly furnished and decorated with paintings and porcelain.

On the ground floor was an entrance hall containing John Hunter's sedan chair. Hunter met his patients in two rooms at the rear of the house.

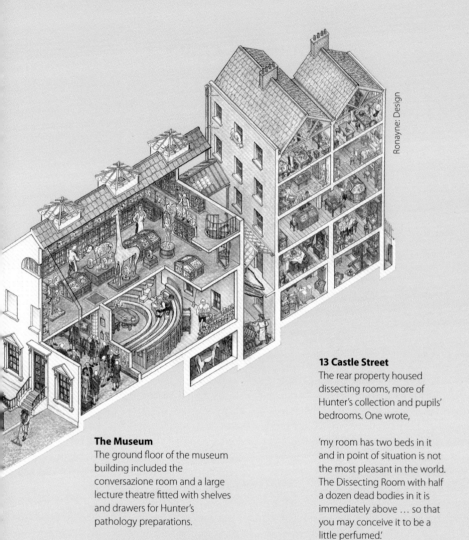

## The Museum
The ground floor of the museum building included the conversazione room and a large lecture theatre fitted with shelves and drawers for Hunter's pathology preparations.

The main museum on the floor above contained thousands more items, including a giraffe and the skeleton of Charles Byrne (the 'Irish Giant'). Hunter's important art collection was also displayed.

## 13 Castle Street
The rear property housed dissecting rooms, more of Hunter's collection and pupils' bedrooms. One wrote,

'my room has two beds in it and in point of situation is not the most pleasant in the world. The Dissecting Room with half a dozen dead bodies in it is immediately above … so that you may conceive it to be a little perfumed.'

# CHAPTER THREE

# Hunter's Legacy

Besides his museum collection and his
contribution to surgery, John Hunter influenced
medical education, dentistry, pathology and
veterinary science.

Despite his fractious relationship with his peers at St George's Hospital, John Hunter was a highly respected surgeon and a popular teacher. He developed new approaches to surgery but was careful only to operate when necessary. Through experiments and observation he was able to show that living tissue could adapt to injury or disease meaning that surgery wasn't always needed and avoiding surgery was, in fact, often the best solution. One patient, for example, had badly fractured his left arm and received no treatment. As a result this arm was six inches shorter than the other but he survived and gradually regained some use of the limb and, more importantly, had not been exposed to a risky operation.

Hunter used the knowledge he gained from his experimental work to improve the

standard of care that he could offer. His research into the growth of deer antlers led to a new treatment for popliteal aneurysm that benefited the coachman whose preserved leg can be seen in the museum. Only by understanding the collateral blood supply and the role that it played in supporting the main arterial system could Hunter develop this new technique.

As a teacher Hunter encouraged his pupils to think for themselves, to trust what they observed of the human body and always to ask questions rather than accepting established doctrine. Hunter's own lectures changed from year to year as his research and experiments developed his understanding.

The most famous of Hunter's pupils was Edward Jenner, who was to pioneer vaccination. Others became leading members of the next generation of British surgery, including Astley Paston Cooper, William Blizard and Henry Cline, all future presidents of the Royal College of Surgeons. Others were instrumental in establishing medical services overseas, including William Shippen and Philip Syng Physick, who both practised in Philadelphia, USA.

John Hunter's precise knowledge of anatomy also contributed to the development of dentistry. He examined countless bones, teeth and jaws while at his brother's anatomy school and his work with the dentist James Spence gave him a deep understanding of tooth decay, disease and dental pain. In *The Natural History of the Human Teeth* (1771) he introduced the terms bicuspids, cuspids, incisors and molars; in the follow-up

*A Practical Treatise on the Diseases of the Teeth* (1778) he detailed dental and oral pathology and described his work on the transplantation of teeth. Preparations he made for this work can be seen in the museum.

John Hunter's fascination with the structure of bodies generally included 'morbid anatomy' or pathology. As well as studying the physical appearance of diseases and the impact they could have, he also asked questions about their causes. He was well known for the quality of his dissection and he performed hundreds of post-mortem examinations on his patients. He was then able to make connections between their symptoms and the physical changes to the tissues and organs he saw in their dead bodies.

**Human Skull**
A syphilitic skull later added to the collection to complement John Hunter's important contribution to morbid anatomy.

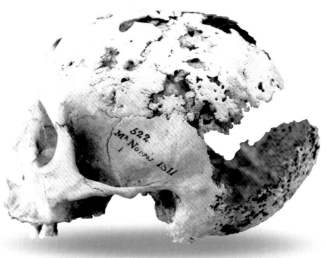

**Crocodile**
A young crocodile, removed
from its egg but still attached to
the umbilical cord, prepared by
John Hunter.

When adding pathological specimens to his
constantly expanding collection, Hunter
therefore took particular care to include
detailed clinical records alongside the
preparations. Together with his casebooks
they provide a valuable insight into the
injuries and diseases common to his patients.
Hunter was an inspiration to his nephew,
Matthew Baillie, who published the first
pathology book in English, *The Morbid
Anatomy of Some of the Most Important Parts
of the Human Body* in 1793, the year of
Hunter's death.

Hunter's influence stretched even beyond the
study of human anatomy and pathology to
zoology. From childhood his passion was the
natural environment and many of his studies
were of animals and birds – especially the
rare species he kept at his country house in
Earl's Court. His zoological work earned him
his Fellowship of the Royal Society in 1767.

It was not unusual for a surgeon to be called
to undertake some veterinary work (the
instrument collection in the museum includes
veterinary tools) and John Hunter was
actively involved in the treatment of live
animals. He was a patron and vice-president
of the London Veterinary College, founded
in 1791, which offered three-year courses in
anatomy, physiology, *materia medica* and
pathology. Like dentists and pathologists,
zoologists and veterinarians consider John
Hunter to be an influential figure. It is no
surprise then to find so much comparative
anatomy in his surviving collection, with
different species displayed side by side.

Having spent more than three decades gathering this museum of human and animal anatomy, Hunter stipulated in his will that it should be sold in its entirety to the government for the public benefit. Hunter saw the collection as his legacy to the nation and the money it would raise as his family's inheritance.

On his death in 1793, however, Britain was at war and there was little money to spare. The collection remained in the Castle Street house where William Clift, John Hunter's assistant, began the painstaking task of cataloguing over 13,000 specimens and sorting and copying Hunter's papers.

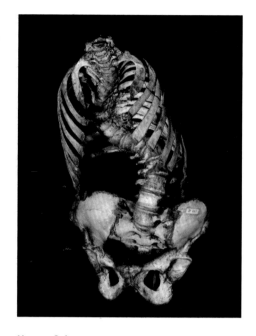

**Human Spine**
This person's spine was twisted forwards and to the right, a painful condition called kyphoscoliosis.

Finally in 1799, after several petitions to Parliament, the government agreed to purchase the collection for £15,000 (it seems that only £2,000 of this was given to Anne Hunter to support her in later life). The Company of Surgeons – soon to become the Royal College of Surgeons – was deemed a worthy guardian and a board of trustees was established that continues to oversee its care today. Clift brought the specimens to the College's new site on Lincoln's Inn Fields in 1807 and they were finally installed in purpose-built galleries in 1813. Hunter may have been a rebellious and difficult surgeon during his lifetime but his collection brought new status to the surgical profession. It marked the beginning of two centuries of dramatic changes in surgery.

**The Royal College of Surgeons**
The expanding College and in particular the Hunterian Museum quickly outgrew its new home in Lincoln's Inn Fields and the building was remodelled and extended in 1834–37 to a design by Charles Barry, the architect of the Bank of England. Here George Scharf shows the rebuilding work in 1834.

# CHAPTER FOUR

# Surgery Transformed

Anaesthetics and asepsis revolutionised patient care in the 19th century as surgery changed from a back-street craft to a clinical science.

The Hunterian collection grew rapidly at the Royal College of Surgeons but the specimens were poorly catalogued. Then in 1827 a young naturalist, Richard Owen, was appointed to assist William Clift as conservator. Owen was a skilled anatomist and palaeontologist who described many new species and would coin 'Dinosauria' to describe the newly discovered prehistoric reptiles. He set about documenting the entire founding collection and several thousand other specimens acquired since Hunter's death.

Owen went on to be the first director of the Natural History Museum in South Kensington, as did one of his successors, William Henry Flower. While at the Hunterian Museum, Flower had carefully re-displayed the museum. He had animal skeletons re-mounted to make it easier for bones to be removed for teaching and

developed the collection of human skulls into a rigorous comparative series.

The museum was not only a significant site for scientific research but also an important resource for teaching surgeons. During the 19th century the College expanded its examining function to play a vital role in medical education as private anatomy schools closed down and the profession became more regulated.

As surgical teaching changed, so did surgical practice. Although John Hunter had encouraged a new way of thinking about surgery, operations changed little during the 18th century. The aim was to finish as quickly as possible before the pain overwhelmed the patient: the Scottish surgeon Robert Liston is said to have amputated a leg in 30 seconds.

This was to change with the advent of anaesthetics. In 1846 an American dentist, William Morton, made a patient unconscious with ether while he extracted teeth. Word of his experiment spread and at University College Hospital in London Robert Liston used ether to carry out an amputation; the operation was over before the patient knew it had begun. 'We have conquered pain!' proclaimed one newspaper. Despite considerable public interest, however, it took some time for other surgeons to be convinced of the benefits of anaesthesia. Even as chloroform was successfully used in the Crimean War, many were cautious of this innovation, preferring their patients to remain alert.

Although anaesthesia allowed for greater care to be taken during operations, removing pain did not increase patients' chances of survival. Mortality rates only began to fall after the second great advance of modern surgery: the development of asepsis, thanks largely to the pioneering antiseptic techniques developed by Joseph Lister.

Like Hunter, Lister was a scientist as well as a surgeon. Born in Essex in 1827, he was the son of a well-known microscope designer – a background that was to have an important influence on his work. Lister trained as a surgeon in London then worked in Edinburgh and Glasgow before making his return to London. He was particularly

**Charlotte Waite's Samplers**
Charlotte Waite, an 11-year-old from Yorkshire, stitched these needlework samplers while recovering from one of the first operations under chloroform in Britain.

**Lister's Spray**
Joseph Lister's device for spraying a fine mist of carbolic acid over an operation to prevent infection was known as the 'donkey engine' – a joke name that comes from the early horse-powered pumps used in mines. The small glass vessel on the top of the device was filled with the acid solution that was pumped into the room.

interested in wound infections, such as gangrene, that posed a constant threat to his patients. He was intrigued by the work of the French scientist, Louis Pasteur, who showed that fermentation was caused by tiny organisms or 'germs', invisible to the naked eye. Lister wondered if the same germs were responsible for wound infections. He carried out many experiments to test his ideas. The microscope and other scientific instruments he used are displayed in the museum.

From 1865 Lister used carbolic acid as an antiseptic agent, first on wound dressings and later sprayed over the entire operation. Surgery at the time was often performed in wealthy patients' homes, or else crowded rooms full of students – all of whom, like the surgeons, were wearing their normal clothes.

**Wax Model by Joseph Towne**
Medical museums were important places for education and alongside the specimens were waxworks such as this one by Joseph Towne of Guy's Hospital.

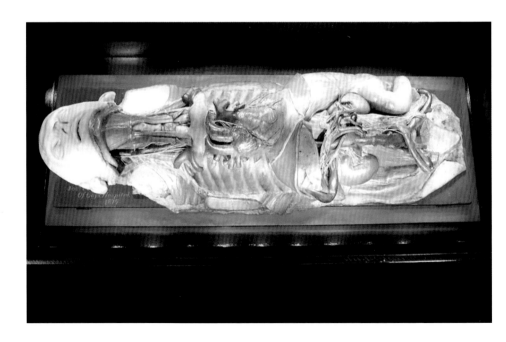

A fine mist of the acid was pumped over the patient, the surgeon and his assistants. It drenched everyone, smelt terrible and caused nasty skin rashes. Many surgeons refused to use it because it was so unpleasant.

Lister's persistence gradually paid off, however. He showed that antisepsis reduced the death rate of his patients from 45% to just 15%. Even those surgeons who doubted the value of carbolic spray came to agree that germs caused infection. The unpopular sprays were replaced by techniques involving steam and sterile instruments. Lister also developed ways of tying off arteries during operations that did not lead to infections as they often had before. He was widely acclaimed for his pioneering work, becoming the first surgeon appointed to the House of Lords, a mark not only of Lister's esteem but also the status of surgery as a profession.

**Robert Koch's Tuberculosis Culture**
These test tube samples of tuberculosis were prepared by the famous German microbiologist Robert Koch, who identified the bacteria in 1882.

By the time Lister died in 1912, surgery had changed beyond recognition. Advances in bacteriology and other sciences helped surgeons to understand infection and disease while anaesthetics, asepsis and other innovations were gradually accepted. They allowed surgeons to perform prolonged, internal procedures and encouraged them to develop new approaches to conditions that were previously considered impossible to treat by surgery. Entire operations were aseptic, with the sterile gloves, masks and gowns that we would recognise today. In the closing decades of the 19th century it seemed to their patients that surgeons could perform miracles.

# Modern Surgery

Over the last century, progress in technology,
drug therapies and biosciences has
fundamentally changed the practice of surgery
and the patient's experience.

The advances of the 19th century were soon tested at the outbreak of World War One in 1914. Out of necessity surgeons became specialised in new techniques that were devised to treat specific areas of the body, including thoracic, orthopaedic and plastic surgery.

The plastic surgeon Harold Gillies (1882–1960) developed new procedures to help reconstruct the faces of badly injured soldiers and airmen. Facial injuries caused by bullet wounds and flying shrapnel needed extensive work on bone, muscle and skin to restore the appearance of the casualties. Gillies grafted patients' own skin and tissue to aid reconstructive surgery and reduce the chance of rejection, very much in the Hunterian tradition. Patients often underwent multiple operations over a number of years.

Henry Tonks (1862–1937), who was both a qualified surgeon and an accomplished artist, worked with Gillies to produce detailed plans of each operation, making diagrammatic drawings of incisions, implants and grafts. Tonks also produced a series of sensitive pastel portraits of the soldiers, which are part of the museum collections.

Harold Gillies's pioneering work inspired his cousin Archibald McIndoe (1900–60), a plastic surgeon who operated during World War Two. McIndoe was faced with different kinds of injuries, mainly airmen who had sustained horrific burns when their planes were shot down. As well as repairing their damaged faces and bodies, McIndoe also promoted their mental wellbeing and formed the Guinea Pig Club to support their rehabilitation.

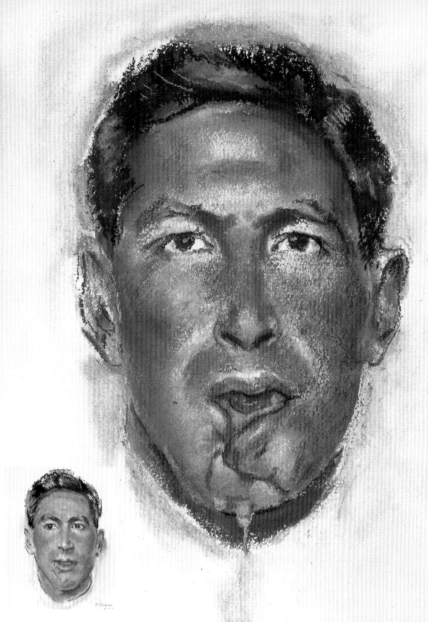

**Henry Tonks's Pastels**
Henry Tonks, an artist and a surgeon, produced a series of
intimate pastel portraits of soldiers injured in the World War One.
These two show Private Sauve, possibly of the 8th Canadian
Infantry, before and after his treatment by the surgeon Harold
Gillies at Queen Mary's Hospital, Sidcup.

**A Devastated Museum**
Museum Room II was relatively unscathed by the bombing in May 1941. Other galleries were completely destroyed.

On the night of 10 May 1941 the College was directly hit by several incendiary bombs. Two-thirds of the collection was lost overnight, including around 10,000 of Hunter's original specimens.

The Hunterian Museum included a 'war museum' during the First World War, when the prominent anatomist and anthropologist Sir Arthur Keith was conservator. By the time he retired in 1933 the museum was internationally acclaimed and its five galleries contained around 65,000 specimens. The sheer size of the museum made it hard to remove from London at the outbreak of renewed hostilities. Parts of the collection were transferred to the specially reinforced basements but the majority remained *in situ.*

After the war, the College's collections were spread across four distinct museums: the Hunterian Museum (what was left of it), new anatomy and pathology teaching collections, and the Odontological Museum (given by the Odontological Section of the Royal Society of Medicine). The College and the post-war surgical profession also became more specialised. To support its fellows and members and meet their in-depth professional requirements, the College focused on research, surgical training and education. Well-equipped laboratories were central to the new buildings erected after the war damage.

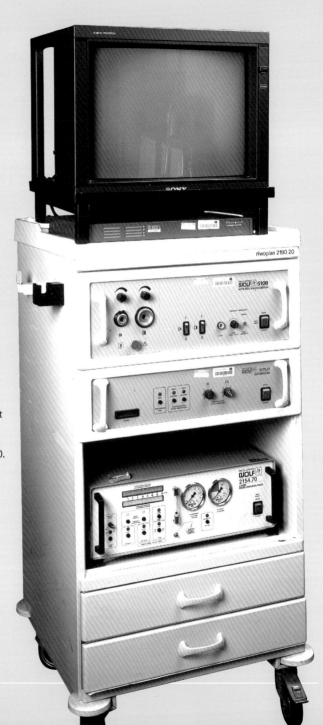

**Minimally Invasive Surgery**
Surgeons began to use minimally invasive or keyhole surgery from the late 1980s. Smaller incisions were less painful, scarred less and were faster to heal. This equipment was used by Mr David Rosin to perform the first laparoscopic gall bladder removal in London in 1990.

Considerable changes in the practice of surgery stemmed from the application of scientific research in new laboratory fields, especially pharmacology, biochemistry and immunology. Physiological and biochemical research led to improvements in anaesthesia and intensive care. These helped surgery on the heart, lungs and brain become established specialties. Antibiotics controlled post-operative infection following increasingly complex procedures performed in these fields.

As surgery became more scientific, surgeons worked with researchers, technicians and instrument companies to introduce new techniques and treatments. From the early 1950s the use of operating microscopes enabled surgeons to repair minute structures. Fibre-optic endoscopes were introduced into surgical practice in the 1960s. Combined with video cameras, they gave rise to a range of minimally invasive techniques that avoided the need for large incisions and greatly benefited patients' recovery.

Ultrasound, computed tomography (CT) and magnetic resonance imaging (MRI) provided new ways for surgeons to locate diseases and injuries within the body. Materials science and bioengineering gave rise to a variety of surgical devices. These ranged from artificial joints, blood vessels and heart valves to heart-lung and dialysis machines that could act as external support to the patient.

The innovations of the late 20th century provided many benefits to patients. New operations offered hope for diseases or injuries that would previously have been fatal. Improvements in anaesthesia and operative techniques meant that patients recovered from operations faster and suffered less discomfort. Safer surgery also made it possible to treat not only life-threatening conditions but also those that affect the quality of patients' lives.

These advanced surgical instruments, technologies and techniques would no doubt have astounded John Hunter. Examples of them can be seen in the new Hunterian Museum that reopened in 2005 after extensive refurbishment.

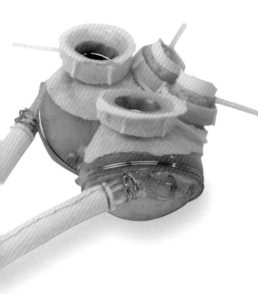

**Akutsu III Artificial Heart**
Implanted by Denton Cooley in Houston, Texas, in 1981, this artificial heart kept the patient alive for 55 hours until a donor heart was found.

# CHAPTER SIX

# The Art of Surgery

Works of art are displayed throughout the building. Collected by John Hunter and later by the College, they depict surgeons, patients and operating scenes, as well as exotic animals.

John and Anne Hunter were friends with many of London's leading artists, including their neighbour Sir Joshua Reynolds (1723–92). Reynolds's portrait of Hunter, now displayed in the College's council chamber, had pride of place in the Hunters' drawing room (see chapter 2).

Many important paintings arrived at the Royal College of Surgeons with Hunter's museum. Still displayed in the College today, these artworks record interesting medical cases, exotic animals and visitors to London from all over the world.

In the 19th and 20th centuries the College continued to collect paintings and drawings of new species or unusual medical conditions. Others provided a record of surgical treatment or showed surgeons at work. To these were added portraits and sculptures commemorating distinguished members, fellows and benefactors of the College.

The College also has collections of silver, ceramics and other decorative arts. The silver includes tableware, commemorative pieces and ceremonial items. The ceramics are mainly 16th to 19th-century drug jars that range from tiny pots for ointments and lozenges to elegant spouted jars for syrups and oils.

Appointments can be made to view artworks not on display in the museum.

**1. *King Henry VIII with the Barber Surgeons* 1541
Studio of Hans Holbein the Younger (1497–1543)**

This large picture shows Henry VIII presenting the charter to the newly formed Company of Barber-Surgeons in 1540. It is very similar to a Holbein work commissioned by the Company, which can still be seen in the Barbers' Hall today. It is believed that the College's version is actually an over-painted preparatory drawing or cartoon for the Barbers' painting. Radiography carried out in the 1960s revealed thousands of tiny prick holes underneath the paint. These were used to transfer the outline of the preparatory drawings on to a wooden panel, on which the final painting was executed.

The figures on the King's right are John Chambers and William Butts, two of his physicians. The man receiving the charter is Thomas Vicary, first Master of the Barber-Surgeons. Through the window in the background the rooftops of London can be seen. A spire dominates the view, thought to be old St Paul's Cathedral, destroyed in the great fire of London in 1666.

**2. *Mary Sabina* c. 1744
unknown artist**

Mary Sabina was born to black African slaves on 12 October 1736 on a Jesuit plantation in the city of Cartagena in what is now Colombia. She had piebaldism, a genetic skin condition present from birth that causes a lack of pigmentation in some parts of the skin and hair. Not much is known about Mary's life but her image became an iconic illustration of this condition. An engraving of Mary in a similar pose to the one shown was used in 1777 to illustrate a volume of the famous *Histoire Naturelle* by George-Louis Leclerc, Comte de Buffon.

Although Mary never came to Europe her picture did and several copies were made. The painting now in the museum travelled from Cartagena to North America, then in 1746 was captured by French privateers while on its way to England. It disappeared for many years but was donated to the museum in 1884 by Sir Erasmus Wilson. Another version of Mary Sabina's portrait can be found in Colonial Williamsburg in the United States.

**3. *Rhinoceros* c. 1792
George Stubbs (1724–1806)**

This Indian rhino was brought to London in 1790 aboard the East India Company ship *Melville Castle*. It was sold to Thomas Clark, a menagerie-keeper who exhibited it at the Lyceum near the Exeter 'Change in the Strand. Stubbs probably made his painting at this time.

In February 1793 Clark sold the animal to Gilbert Pidcock, another menagerie keeper. It was an astute move by Clark, since the animal died a few months later. Undeterred, Pidcock exhibited the stuffed skin for several years.

This painting was owned by John Hunter and was among those displayed in his museum in

1.

2.

3.

4.

5.

Leicester Square. George Stubbs is best known for his depictions of horses but he was also a skilled dissector. Both John and William Hunter commissioned paintings by him because he could portray anatomy accurately, so much so that they used some of his works to illustrate their lectures. Further Stubbs paintings in the College show other exotic animals studied by Hunter – a yak, a drill and an albino baboon.

## 4. *Private Thomas Walker* 1856
## Thomas William Wood (active 1855-72)

Thomas Walker was a Private in the 95th Regiment of Foot at the Battle of Inkerman in the Crimea in 1854. He was wounded in the head and underwent an operation to insert a silver plate in place of a missing piece of bone. Walker returned to the hospital at Fort Pitt in Chatham and was one of the patients visited by Queen Victoria on 3 March 1855.

It is likely that conditions in the Fort Pitt Hospital were good (at least when Victoria visited). However, the painting also served as propaganda at a time when the unsanitary conditions of hospitals in the Crimea caused public concern. This painting, by contrast, shows a model hospital with fresh bedding and a comfortable patient, engaged in a productive and useful activity. It was engraved and reproduced with details of the Queen's visit and accounts of Walker's case in popular journals and newspapers at the time, earning Walker a brief moment of celebrity.

## 5. *Concourse (2)* 1948
## Barbara Hepworth (1903–75)

*Concourse (2)* was inspired by surgeon Norman Capener and his colleagues at the Princess Elizabeth Orthopaedic Hospital in Exeter. Capener first met Hepworth in 1943 while he was treating her daughter Sarah. They became friends and Capener invited Hepworth to observe a number of operations. She made a series of drawings on coloured boards and subsequently several larger works. This is the only one for which she used oils. Hepworth painted the work on to two pine panels given to her by Capener.

Completed in the same year that the National Health Service was founded, the picture embodies the idea of social cohesion and co-operative endeavour that underpinned the social reforms of the post-war era. Describing the works she produced during this period, Hepworth commented on 'the extraordinary beauty of purpose and co-ordination' of the surgical team and said that the composition of the works reflected the sense of unity demonstrated by the surgeons and nurses.

# CHAPTER SEVEN

# Archives

The manuscripts and records in the archives
of the Royal College of Surgeons contain
fascinating insights into the development of
surgery and the surgical profession.

The archives reveal the inner workings of the Royal College of Surgeons, and the surgical profession in general, from its roots in the Company of Barber-Surgeons to the complex medical politics of the 21st century. The College's own records sit alongside papers and manuscripts from key individuals and institutions. These 'deposited' collections were bought, donated or bequeathed to the College, and some date back to the 16th century. They include the personal papers and case notes of surgeons, hospital records, collections of correspondence and individual items such as diaries, photograph albums, lecture notes, drawings and even recipe books.

As a central part of the College, many records relate to the Hunterian Museum. William Clift, first conservator of the new

museum, was a prolific record keeper and his diaries are a valuable resource for information about the workings of the museum and the College. Clift's son-in-law and successor, Richard Owen, left manuscripts relating to cataloguing and other improvements to the collection, and Sir Arthur Keith's groundbreaking scientific work carried out in the museum in the 20th century is reflected in his extensive archive.

Letters exchanged between eminent surgeons and fellow medical professionals, scientists and other important figures are especially revealing. A collection created by John Hunter's sisters and his nephew, the anatomist Matthew Baillie, contains over 1,000 letters from many prominent members of society including Sir Walter Scott, William Wordsworth and Henry Irving.

Dear Jenner

I rec'd yours in answer to mine, which I should have answer'd. I own I suspected it would not be; yet as I did intend such a scheme, I was inclinable to give you the offer. I thank you for your Exp't on the Hedge Hog; but why do you ask me a question, by the way of solving it. I think your solution is just; but why think, why not try the Exp't. Repeat all the Exp't upon a Hedge Hog as soon as you receive this, and they will give you the solution. I'm the
But

**Letter from John Hunter to Edward Jenner c. 1775**

Jenner was a pupil of Hunter's in 1770–72. They shared an enthusiasm for natural history and continued to correspond on many subjects until Hunter's death in 1793.

This letter refers to Jenner's experiments on hedgehogs, their hibernation shedding light on the measurement of body temperatures for survival.

**The Western Friendly Medical Club, 1862–1952**
This club was formed for the purpose of 'establishing and maintaining a sociable and convivial intercourse among its members'.

This collection also features papers relating to the activities of the Hunter-Baillie family and poetry by Anne Hunter.

No history of surgery would be complete without careful attention to medical education and the archives contain lecture notes not only from John Hunter himself but also those of his former pupils John Abernethy and Henry Cline. Personal papers and case notes of Cline's student Sir Astley Paston Cooper along with those of antisepsis pioneer Sir Joseph Lister and Leeds surgeon Sir Berkeley (later Lord) Moynihan tell the inside story of 19th and 20th-century surgery. Complementing the museum collections relating to the First World War are Sir Antony Bowlby's journals documenting his army medical service work and Harold Burrows's photographs of facial repairs carried out while he worked with the military.

History is as much about everyday work as it is about famous figures and the archives hold the records of a number of hospitals and other organisations. The attendance books of the Western Friendly Medical Club include topical and entertaining illustrations. Fine details of surgical practice can be found in the minutes of the West London Medico-Chirurgical Society, the British Society of Dental Surgeons and the Cardiothoracic Society. The archives of the London Lock Hospital, where venereal diseases were treated, include graphic colour drawings of 19th and 20th-century patients showing their symptoms. Small collections of material relating to other hospitals are available, including the Fountain Mental Hospital and a case book from Deptford Hospital Asylum.

Among the surgery-related material – such as the proofs of the engravings for the first edition of Gray's Anatomy – some unexpected items can be found. There are two recipe books compiled in the 17th century that record family remedies for many problems, from burns and the plague to hair dyes. An 18th-century treatise on diseases and treatments from what is now Sri Lanka is written in Pali language on palm leaves. The early 19th-century diary of Joshua Naples is a chilling read: Naples was a grave-robber, or 'resurrectionist', who supplied anatomy schools with corpses before

there was provision for cadavers for medical education. The signature books of the Old Black Jack Public House were signed by young surgeons in the late 19th century upon becoming members of the nearby College.

The majority of the 600 deposited collections have been catalogued and details can be found on the College website; visitors can make an appointment to see them. The archive is regularly used by students, writers, artists and genealogists, and its treasures often feature in publications and on television.

**Examination Book, 1831–55**
The College's archives contain many volumes like this which detail its own institutional history.

# CHAPTER EIGHT

# Instruments

The historical instrument collection
highlights major developments in surgical
practice over the past 400 years, showing how
materials and design changed. Many
belonged to renowned surgeons.

Donations of instruments to the College were
recorded as early as 1804. Although many
were destroyed by the bombing in 1941, the
collection now contains over 9,000 items. A
small proportion is displayed in the
Hunterian Museum and the rest are available
for teaching and research. Surgical
equipment from all over the world may be
seen, with examples from Europe, North
America, Asia and Africa. The earliest
instruments date back to the 17th century
and new items are still collected to reflect
changes in modern surgical practice.

Features of the collection include instruments
used by famous surgeons such as Robert
Liston and Harold Gillies, and the scientific
apparatus of Joseph Lister. These include
some of Lister's prototype carbolic sprays
and samples of the catgut ligatures that he

developed, as well as his microscope and glass
vessels used in his experiments on
fermentation.

A range of surgical specialties and procedures
is represented in the collection. Until the late
19th century surgery was mainly limited to
superficial operations on the extremities of
the body. Trepanation (boring a hole in the
skull) is one of the earliest documented
surgical procedures. Most commonly used to
treat depressed skull fractures, archaeological
evidence shows that it was first performed at
least 12,000 years ago. The museum holds
trepanation instruments dating from the 17th
to the 20th centuries.

The collection includes numerous
amputation sets. Amputation is undertaken
for incurable trauma and for infections and

diseases of the limb that threaten the
patient's life. Although the primary objective
is to remove this threat, since the 17th
century techniques have focused on salvaging
function and leaving comfortable stumps for
prostheses. Controlling blood loss is a vital
part of such surgery and the museum holds a
variety of instruments developed for this
purpose. Tourniquets applied compression
and stemmed the flow of blood. Vessels were
sealed with cauteries, tied off with ligatures
or crushed with artery forceps.

Cutting for bladder stones (lithotomy) was
another common operation. The bladder was
accessed through an incision made in the
abdomen or close to the anus. In the early
19th century an alternative, lithotrity, was
introduced. An early example of minimally
invasive surgery, this involved crushing or
drilling the stone with a long instrument
inserted via the urethra.

Historical treatments were sometimes
counter-productive. Despite actually
weakening patients, blood letting was used to
treat a range of disorders and remained
common practice until the late 19th century.
A patient could lose up to a pint and a half
of blood at each sitting.

The instrument collection reflects the
major surgical advances of the 19th and
20th centuries. Early anaesthetic apparatus
heralded an era of reduced pain and distress
for the patient. In the wake of asepsis new
surgical specialties emerged that are
represented by instruments devoted to the
surgery on the gastro-intestinal system,
brain, heart and lungs.

The introduction of thermal sterilisation
brought changes to the materials used for
instruments. Pre-aseptic devices were often
elaborately decorated, with intricately carved
handles made from expensive materials such
as ebony, lignum vitae, mother of pearl, ivory
and horn. Sterilisation prompted the need for
corrosion-resistant instruments; nickel and
chrome plating was used from the 1880s and
stainless steel from the 1920s.

In recent decades, minimally invasive surgery
has been an increasingly important field. The
instrument collection includes examples of
flexible endoscopes (used to view body
cavities through natural orifices) and
laparoscopes (used to view the abdomen
through surgical incisions).

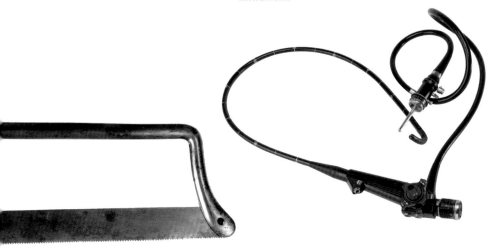

### Amputation Saw

From a late 18th century
amputation set. The surgeon cut
soft tissue with a knife then used
the saw on bone.

### Gastroscope

This flexible gastroscope dates from the late
20th century. The tube was passed through
the mouth to examine the oesophagus and
stomach.

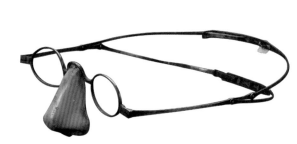

### Clockwork Bone Saw

There was no way of stopping or
regulating the speed of this mid
19th century prototype. Not
surprisingly, it failed to catch on.

### Silver Prosthetic Nose

This was worn by a 19th-century woman who
lost her nose because of syphilis. On
remarrying she abandoned it, declaring that
her new husband preferred her without it.

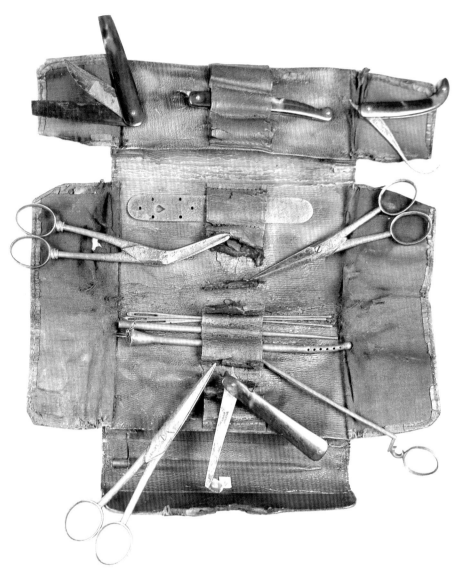

**Pocket Set**

Surgical instruments carried by the explorer Mungo Park (1771–1806) on his first expedition to Africa in the 1790s. The case contains scissors, lancets and probes; the horizontal device towards the bottom of the case is a female catheter. Park gave the set to the surgeon Sir Anthony Carlisle, one of the Hunterian Museum's curators and later President of the Royal College of Surgeons.

# CHAPTER NINE

# The Odontological Collection

There are over 11,000 skulls and teeth in the odontological collection. Alongside human jaws are animal remains including gigantic elephant tusks and delicate bird crania.

The Royal College of Surgeons has held an extensive dental ('odontological') collection since the early 20th century. Originally accumulated by dentists, the collection was intended to focus on the development of the skull and teeth. Over the years, specimens were assembled to show a range of diseases and the general patterns of growth. Two-thirds of the collection is made up from animal material, which includes common domesticated species to rare and even extinct creatures. The human material contributes to our understanding of dental development and malformations.

Care of these items had been transferred between different societies and museums before arriving at the College. When disaster struck in 1941 and the Hunterian collection was badly bombed, the odontological specimens escaped largely unscathed as they were stored in the basement. After the war, the collection was displayed in a small museum next to the Hunterian Museum. Some of the material is now integrated into the Hunterian displays, while the majority of specimens form a research collection.

Items of specific historical interest can still be seen in the museum, such as the short twine necklace of 38 human teeth brought back from the Congo River by the explorer Henry Morton Stanley (1841–1904), or the selection of teeth retrieved from soldiers who perished during the battle of Waterloo in 1815. Approximately 400 of the human skulls have been donated as a result of archaeological excavations from sites around the world. Although donations have decreased over the past century, one of the more recent

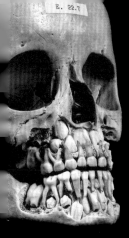

**Juvenile Skull**
This child was aged around 6 years at death. The surface bone has been removed to show the adult teeth developing within the jaw.

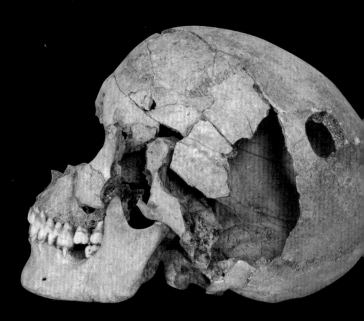

**Trepanned Roman Skull**
Excavated from a Romano-British site dating to 400AD, this skull shows a rare example of trepanation. Unfortunately for the patient this operation was probably the cause of death.

**Winston Churchill's Dentures**
Made in the 1940s, this partial upper denture worn by Churchill was reportedly designed to maintain his famous lisp.

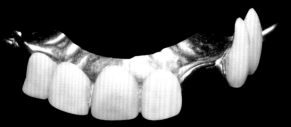

acquisitions was Sir Winston Churchill's upper denture, designed by his dentist Wilfred Fish.

Many mammals, birds, fish and reptile skulls further enhance the variety of the collection. The mammal collection is the largest, stretching from the colossal killer whale to the tiny fruit bat. The 3,000 primate skulls range from the biggest on earth, the mountain gorilla, to one of the smallest, the mouse lemur. Such comparative anatomy is a major theme that has endured for over 150 years. All of the odontological material is documented and can be searched online; access for research can be arranged upon request.

**Twisted Elephant Tusk**
An unusual example of a malformed tusk, which may have grown in a spiral shape as a result of injury to the jaws.